6

Zaner-Bloser
Handwriting

Author
Clinton S. Hackney, Ed.D.

Reviewers

Julie Althide, Teacher, Hazelwood School District, St. Louis, Missouri

Becky Brashears, Teacher, Gocio Elementary, Sarasota, Florida

Douglas Dewey, Teacher, National Heritage Academies, Grand Rapids, Michigan

Jennifer B. Dutcher, Teacher, Elk Grove School District, Sacramento, California

Gita Farbman, Teacher, School District of Philadelphia, Philadelphia, Pennsylvania

Susan Ford, Teacher, St. Ann's School, Charlotte, North Carolina

Brenda Forehand, Teacher, David Lipscomb Middle School, Nashville, Tennessee

Sharon Hall, Teacher, USD 443, Dodge City, Kansas

Sr. James Madeline, Teacher, St. Anthony School, Allston, Massachusetts

Lori A. Martin, Teacher, Chicago Public Schools, Chicago, Illinois

Vikki F. McCurdy, Teacher, Mustang School District, Oklahoma City, Oklahoma

Melissa Neary Morgan, Reading Specialist, Fairfax County Public Schools, Fairfax, Virginia

Sue Postlewait, Literacy Resource Consultant, Marshall County Schools, Moundsville, West Virginia

Gloria C. Rivera, Principal, Edinburg CISO, Edinburg, Texas

Rebecca Rollefson, Teacher, Ericsson Community School, Minneapolis, Minnesota

Susan Samsa, Teacher, Dover City Schools, Dover, Ohio

Zelda J. Smith, Instructional Specialist, New Orleans Public Schools, New Orleans, Louisiana

Occupational Therapy Consultant: Maureen E. King, O.T.R.

Credits

Art: Diane Blasius: 52; Liz Callen: 46, 47; John Hovell: 22, 25, 29, 32, 36, 53, 54, 55, 62; Tom Leonard: 3, 30, 31, 35, 43, 53, 56, 58, 60; Sharron O'Neil: 3, 4, 5, 11, 14, 18, 38, 57

Photos: George C. Anderson Photography, Inc.: 4; Dallas & John Heaton/Corbis: 50; Conrad Zobel/Corbis: 49

Literature: "Metaphor," from A SKY FULL OF POEMS by Eve Merriam. Copyright © 1964, 1970, 1973 by Eve Merriam. All rights renewed and reserved. Used by permission of Marian Reiner.

Development: Kirchoff/Wohlberg, Inc., in collaboration with Zaner-Bloser Educational Publishers

ISBN-13 978-0-7367-5149-0
ISBN-10 0-7367-5149-1

07 08 09 10 11 4495 5 4 3 2 1

Zaner-Bloser, Inc., P.O. Box 16764, Columbus, Ohio 43216-6764
1-800-421-3018
www.zaner-bloser.com
Printed in the United States of America

Contents

*An Exhibition of
Art and Poetry
By Mr. Davy's
Sixth Grade
Class
Friday,
October 21,
2:00-4:00
Prizes will
be awarded!*

You write for many reasons at school, at home, and in your community. The lessons in this book will help you write legibly so you and other people can easily read what you have written.

Evaluating your own handwriting is a good habit to form. When you see the **Stop and Check** sign in this book, stop and circle the best letter or joining you wrote on that line.

You will see the **Keys to Legibility** throughout this book. They will help you remember to check the **shape, size, spacing,** and **slant** of your writing to make sure it is easy to read.

4

On your paper, write this poem in your best cursive handwriting.

Circle your three best letters. Underline three letters that need improvement.

Metaphor

Morning is
a new sheet of paper
for you to write on.

Whatever you want to
say,
all day,
until night
folds it up
and files it away.

The bright words and
the dark words
are gone
until dawn
and a new day
to write on.

Eve Merriam

5

Writing Positions and Basic Strokes

Sit comfortably with your feet flat on the floor.
Rest both arms on the desk. Shift your paper as you write.

Paper Position

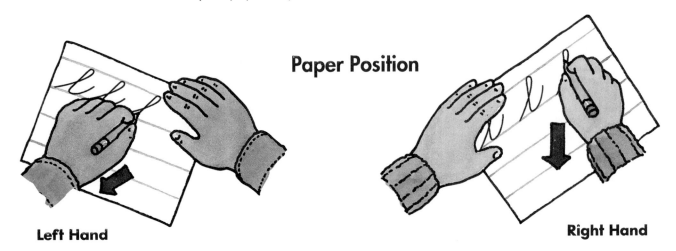

Left Hand

Right Hand

Pencil Position

Rest the pencil near your big knuckle.

Point the pencil
toward your left elbow.

Hold the pencil with your first
two fingers and thumb.

Point the pencil
toward your right shoulder.

Bend your
thumb.

Left Hand

Rest your last two fingers
on the paper.

Right Hand

Practice the basic cursive strokes.

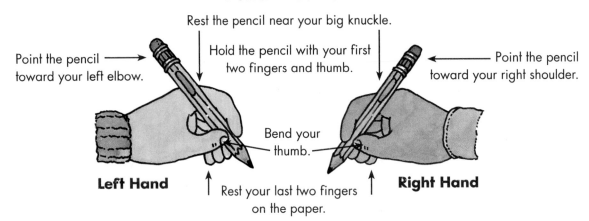

Undercurve

Downcurve

Overcurve

Slant

Cursive Letters and Numerals

Aa Bb Cc Dd Ee Ff Gg
Hh Ii Jj Kk Ll Mm
Nn Oo Pp Qq Rr Ss Tt
Uu Vv Ww Xx Yy Zz
1 2 3 4 5 6 7 8 9 10

Write some letters that have undercurves _____.

_____

Write some letters that have downcurves _____.

_____

Write some letters that have overcurves _____.

_____

Write some letters that have slant strokes _____.

_____

Write the letters and numerals you already write well.

_____

_____

Write the letters and numerals you want to improve.

_____

_____

Keys to Legibility

Shape

As you write cursive, pay attention to the shape of your letters.

Some letters have undercurve strokes.   _u_   _e_   _b_   _f_   _R_

Some letters have downcurve strokes.   _a_   _o_   _c_   _a_   _D_

Some letters have overcurve strokes.   _x_   _y_   _z_   _I_   _Q_

Some letters have slant strokes.   _d_   _h_   _m_   _B_

Size

You should also pay attention to the size of your writing.

Tall letters should not touch the headline.

Some lowercase letters are tall letters.   _d_   _h_   _l_

All uppercase letters are tall letters.   _a_   _T_   _S_

Short letters should be half the height of tall letters.

Many lowercase letters are short letters.   _c_   _g_   _m_

Descenders should not go too far below the baseline.

Some letters have descenders.   _g_   _f_   _q_   _z_

Write the sentence. Pay attention to the shape and size of your letters.

Each letter has good shape and size.

Spacing

Your writing should have good spacing.

Leave space for O between letters.

letters

Leave space for \ between words.

word \ word

Leave space for O between sentences.

end. O Begin

Write the sentences. Then draw O between letters, \ between words, and O between sentences to check your spacing.

This spacing is correct. Shift your paper as you write.

Slant

The slant of your writing should be uniform.

All your letters should slant forward.

Check the slant. Draw lines through the slant strokes of the letters.

Are your lines parallel?

Write the sentence. Pay careful attention to shape, size, spacing, and slant.

This is my best handwriting.

Write Undercurve Letters

Write the letters, joinings, and words.

i   *i*   *i*   *i*   *i*   *i*   *i*

it   *is*   *ic*   *ig*   *im*   *in*

igloo   *insistent*   *import*

eternity   *musical*   *surprise*

t   *t*   *t*   *t*   *t*   *t*   *t*

tr   *th*   *ta*   *to*   *ty*   *tm*

treasury   *takeoff*   *total*

withdraw   *hearty*   *apartment*

Better Letters

Pull slant strokes to the baseline. Write:

i not *i*   *t* not *t*

✔ Check your writing folder. Do you pull slant strokes
to the baseline?   Yes   No

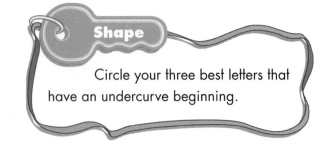

Shape

Circle your three best letters that
have an undercurve beginning.

Write the letters, joinings, and words.

u   u   u   u   u   u   u   ✓

up   us   ua   ug   un   um   ✓

user   upstream   unsure

punctual   thump   although

w   w   w   w   w   w   w   ✓

wr   ws   wo   wa   wn   wy   ✓

warbler   worthwhile   writing

lawyer   download   browse

Better *Letters*

Make slant strokes parallel. Write:

u not u   w not w

✔ Check your writing folder. Are your slant strokes parallel?   Yes   No

Write Undercurve Letters

Write the letters, joinings, and words.

e   *e*   *e*   *e*   *e*   *e*   *e*

et   *es*   *ea*   *ed*   *em*   *en*

edge   *earphones*   *demonstrate*

fend   *forgetful*   *nestle*

l   *l*   *l*   *l*   *l*   *l*   *l*

li   *lu*   *la*   *ld*   *ly*   *lv*

luxury   *lament*   *likeable*

foothold   *perfectly*   *revolve*

Better *Letters*

End the loop with a slant stroke. Write:

e not *ℓ*   *l* not *ℓ*

✔ Check your writing folder. Do you write these letters
correctly?   Yes   No

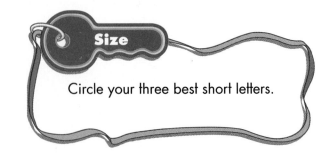

Size

Circle your three best short letters.

Write the letters, joinings, and words.

b   b   b   b   b   b   b

br   bu   ba   bo   by   bm

boost   bumble   brink

h   h   h   h   h   h   h

he   hi   ht   ha   ho   hy

haiku   hesitant   historic

f   f   f   f   f   f   f

fe   fl   fr   fa   fo   fy

flu   falcon   identify

Better Letters

Make the first undercurve deep enough to keep the loop open. Write:

b not b   h not h   f not f

✔ Check your writing folder.
Are your loops open?   Yes   No

Size

Circle your three best tall letters.

Write Undercurve Letters

Write the letters, joinings, and words.

k   k   k   k   k   k   k

ke   ki   ka   ko   kn   ky

kennel   kin   knapsack

r   r   r   r   r   r   r

re   rt   ra   ro   rn   ry

reliable   rascal   modern

s   s   s   s   s   s   s

sh   st   sa   so   sn   sy

shoreline   starfish   sound

Better Letters

Pause after the first undercurve to avoid loops. Write:

r not r   s not s

✔ Check your writing folder. Do you write these letters
without loops?   Yes   No

14

Write the letters, joinings, and words.

j   j   j   j   j   j   j

je   ji   ju   ja   jo

jubilant   jest   jingle

major   injury   deejay

p   p   p   p   p   p   p

pi   pl   po   pa   py   pn

pastime   plateau   pyramid

epic   oppose   sharpness

Better Letters

End **j** with an overcurve, and end **p** with an undercurve. Write:

j not j   p not p

✔ Check your writing folder. Do you end these letters correctly ?   Yes   No

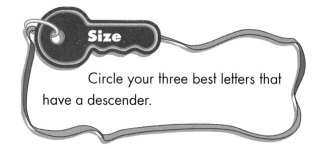

Size

Circle your three best letters that have a descender.

Adjectives

You use adjectives to make your writing more interesting.
Write an adjective from the box to describe each item.

unusual	*spectacular*	*humorous*
terrific	*joyful*	*weird*
incredible	*wonderful*	*pleasant*
fabulous	*elegant*	*beautiful*

1. _____ books   7. _____ gifts

2. _____ sweaters   8. _____ songs

3. _____ sports   9. _____ movies

4. _____ sneakers   10. _____ days

5. _____ stories   11. _____ plans

6. _____ news   12. _____ designs

Now write a sentence that includes two of the phrases you wrote above.

_____

_____

_____

Keys to Legibility

My writing has good shape. ☐
My writing has good size. ☐

Writing Legibly
Joinings

I. Study these tips for writing clear, legible joinings between letters.

✔ For letters with **undercurve** endings, the undercurve swings wide to begin the next letter.

undercurve to undercurve: write *qu*, not *qu*.

undercurve to downcurve: write *ho*, not *ho*.

✔ For letters with **overcurve** endings, the overcurve crosses at the baseline and swings up to begin the next letter.

overcurve to undercurve: write *ji*, not *ji*.

overcurve to overcurve: write *zy*, not *zy*.

✔ For letters with **checkstroke** endings, the checkstroke swings right to begin the next letter.

checkstroke to undercurve: write *ol*, not *ol*.

checkstroke to downcurve: write *va*, not *va*.

2. Look at this part of a student's vocabulary paper. Underline joinings that need improvement.

lava: hot liquid rock that comes from a volcano when it erupts

3. Rewrite the student's work correctly, then write the definition for one of your own vocabulary or spelling words. Pay attention to the tips for legible joinings.

Write Downcurve Letters

Write the letters, joinings, and words.

a

a   *a*   *a*   *a*   *a*   *a*   *a*

at   as   ad   ag   an   ax

astray   attitude   agile

canteen   meadow   taxes

d

d   *d*   *d*   *d*   *d*   *d*   *d*

dr   dw   di   dg   dd   dn

dwelling   dramatic   couldn't

edition   smudge   addition

Better Letters

Don't loop **a** and **d**. Write:

a not *a*   d not *d*

✔ Check your writing folder. Do you write these letters
   without loops?   Yes   No

Write the letters, joinings, and words.

g ✔

gu   gh   ga   gg   gy   gn ✔

galaxy   guardian   align

height   apology   luggage

o

o ✔

ou   os   od   oc   ov   on ✔

prosper   document   overlap

outcome   nobody   headlong

Spacing

Circle three words you wrote
that have good joinings.

Write Downcurve Letters

Write the letters, joinings, and words.

c   c   c   c   c   c   c

ct   cl   ch   co   ca   cy

category   cherish   encounter

prediction   bicycle   incline

q   q   q   q   q   q   q

qu   qu   qu   qu   qu   qu

quest   quantity   equality

squad   bouquet   aquatic

Better Letters

Begin **c** and **q** with a downcurve. Write:

c not c   q not q

✔ Check your writing folder. Are your downcurve letters smooth and rounded?   Yes   No

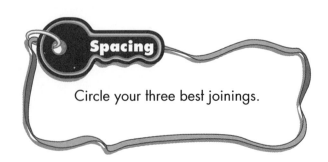

Spacing

Circle your three best joinings.

Practice
Frequently Confused Words

principal	allowed	clique
altogether	attendance	boulder
assistants	compliment	council
wood	ring	overseas

Homophones are words that are frequently confused because they sound alike but have different spellings and different meanings. Write a homophone for each word below.

principle

wring

counsel

would

aloud

complement

all together

oversees

click

bolder

assistance

attendants

Now write a sentence that includes two frequently confused words.

Manuscript Maintenance

Food, Food, Food!

The following is a list of foods. Below the list is a diagram of the food pyramid.
Each day people should choose more food from the groups near the
bottom of the pyramid than from the groups near the top of the pyramid.
Write the words from the list under each group heading. Write in manuscript.

cereal	carrots	cheese	hamburger	yogurt
pears	ravioli	green beans	macaroni	apples
milk	oatmeal	candy bar	potatoes	butter
chicken	bread	rice	eggs	squash

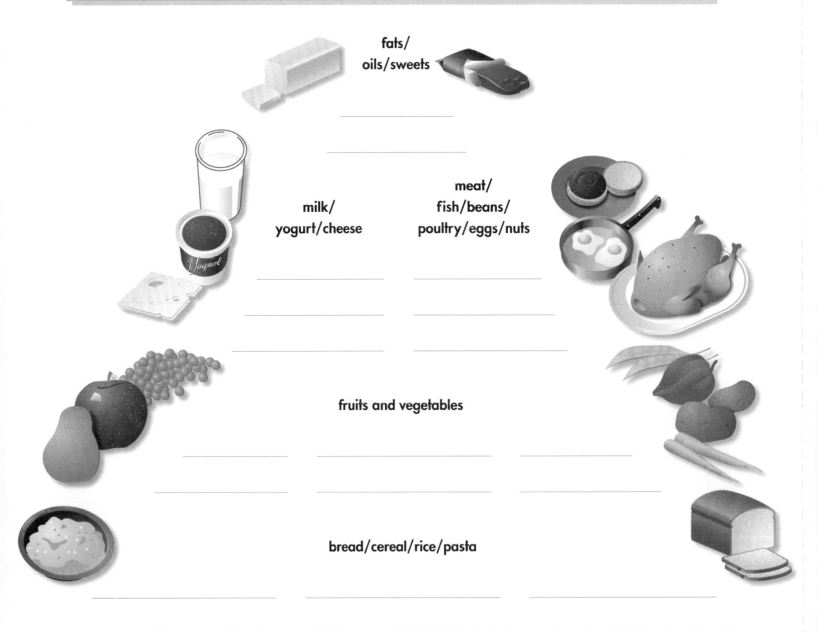

**fats/
oils/sweets**

_____

_____

**milk/
yogurt/cheese**

**meat/
fish/beans/
poultry/eggs/nuts**

_____ _____

_____ _____

fruits and vegetables

_____

_____

bread/cereal/rice/pasta

_____

_____

Write Overcurve Letters

Write the letters, joinings, and words.

n

n   n   n   n   n   n   n ✓

ni   nk   no   ng   nn   ny ✓

niece   notation   rank

ceremony   findings   biannual

m

m   m   m   m   m   m   m ✓

mp   mb   ma   mo   mm   my ✓

margin   impact   enemy

somber   grammar   remote

Better *Letters*

Remember to round overcurves at the top. Write:

n not *n*   *m* not *m*

✔ Check your writing folder. Are your overcurve letters smooth and rounded?   Yes   No

Slant

Circle three letters you wrote that have good slant.

Write Overcurve Letters

Write the letters, joinings, and words.

y   *y*   *y*   *y*   *y*   *y*   *y*   *y*

ye   *ys*   *yo*   *ya*   *yz*   *yn*

yolk   *yearly*   *yam*

analyze   *days*   *dynamic*

x   *x*   *x*   *x*   *x*   *x*   *x*   *x*

xi   *xh*   *xc*   *xa*   *xo*   *xy*

xylophone   *except*   *taxation*

exhale   *fixing*   *exotic*

Slant

Circle three words you wrote that have good slant.

24

Write the letters, joinings, and words.

v   v   v   v   v   v   v

ve   vi   va   vo   vy

varnish   vertical   voter

aviation   evaporate   gravy

z   z   z   z   z   z   z

zu   zi   zo   za   zz   zy

zoology   zany   amazing

fuzzy   drizzle   azure

Better Letters

Position the paper properly for good slant. Write:

v not v   z not z

✔ Check your writing folder. Do your letters have uniform slant?   Yes   No

AZURE BLUE

Practice
Adverbs

In the box below are some common adverbs. Adverbs are used to modify verbs.

easily	smoothly	reliably	well
quietly	carefully	slowly	neatly

Circle the adverb in each sentence. Then write the complete sentence.

1. Computers work well.

2. They hold data reliably.

3. The mouse glides smoothly.

4. I input my work slowly.

5. Then I read my work carefully.

6. I fix any mistakes easily.

7. The printer prints quietly.

8. My reports are printed neatly.

Keys to Legibility

My writing has good shape. ☐
My writing has good size. ☐
My writing has good spacing. ☐
My writing has good slant. ☐

Writing Legibly
Joinings

1. **Study** these tips for writing clear, legible joinings between letters.

  ✔ For letters with **undercurve** endings, the undercurve swings wide to begin the next letter.

   undercurve to undercurve: write *ni*, not *ni*.

   undercurve to overcurve: write *rm*, not *rm*.

  ✔ For letters with **overcurve** endings, the overcurve crosses at the baseline and swings up to begin the next letter.

   overcurve to undercurve: write *gr*, not *gr*.

   overcurve to downcurve: write *ya*, not *ya*.

  ✔ For letters with **checkstroke** endings, the checkstroke swings right to begin the next letter.

   checkstroke to undercurve: write *ov*, not *ov*.

   checkstroke to overcurve: write *ov*, not *ov*.

2. **Look** at these notes for a student's report. Underline joinings that need improvement.

A computer is an electronic machine that can store a great amount of information.

3. **Rewrite** the student's notes correctly, then write some of your own class notes. Pay attention to the tips for legible joinings.

Write Downcurve Letters

Write the letters, joinings, and words.

a   a   a   a   a   a   a   a

Al   Af   Ae   Ad   Ac   Am

Alabama   African   Aegean

Adriatic   Acapulco   American

O   O   O   O   O   O   O   O

Ohio   Ottawa   Oakland

Okinawa   Odessa   Atlantic Ocean

DID YOU KNOW?

The Atlantic Ocean can be cold.

Better Letters

Swing wide for downcurve strokes. Write:

a not u   O not v

✔ Check your writing folder. Do you write these
letters correctly?   Yes   No

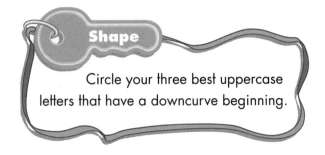

Shape

Circle your three best uppercase
letters that have a downcurve beginning.

Write the letters, joinings, and words.

$\mathcal{D}$ $\mathcal{D}$ $\mathcal{D}$ $\mathcal{D}$ $\mathcal{D}$ $\mathcal{D}$ $\mathcal{D}$ $\mathcal{D}$

Detroit   Dusseldorf   Dijon

Dakar is the capital of Senegal.

$\mathcal{C}$ $\mathcal{C}$ $\mathcal{C}$ $\mathcal{C}$ $\mathcal{C}$ $\mathcal{C}$ $\mathcal{C}$ $\mathcal{C}$

Ch   Cr   Ca   Co   Cz   Cy

Catalonia   Czech   Cyprus

$\mathcal{E}$ $\mathcal{E}$ $\mathcal{E}$ $\mathcal{E}$ $\mathcal{E}$ $\mathcal{E}$ $\mathcal{E}$ $\mathcal{E}$

El   Eu   Ed   Eg   En   Ex

Elba   Edinburgh   Exeter

Better *Letters*

Make sure letters are legible. Write:

$\mathcal{D}$ not $\mathcal{D}$ $\mathcal{E}$ not $\mathcal{E}$

✔ Check your writing folder. Do you write these
letters correctly?   Yes   No

WEST AFRICA

MAURITANIA

SENEGAL

•DAKAR

GAMBIA

GUINEA-BISSAU

GUINEA

29

Practice
Present and Past Tense Verbs

The following sentences have verbs in the present tense. Write the sentences, using the **past tense** of the verb shown in red.

Arthur Conan Doyle creates Sherlock Holmes, the first great detective.

Sandra Cisneros writes poems and stories.

Emily Dickinson is a poet.

O'Henry wrote many stories. He often gives them surprise endings.

Readers like Scott O'Dell's Island of the Blue Dolphins.

Manuscript Maintenance
Constellations

Read the notes a student took on the constellations.
Use the information to complete the chart below.
Write in manuscript.

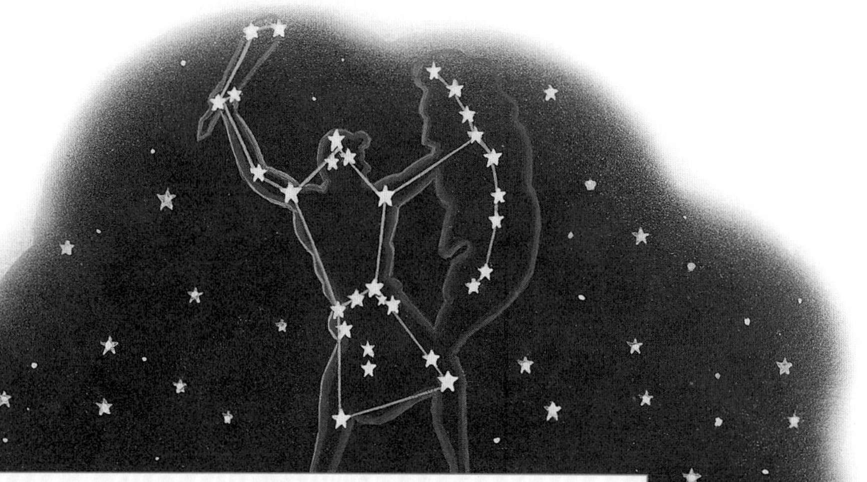

Auriga - northern sky - means "chariot driver"

Equuleus - means "little horse" - northern sky

Orion - southern sky - "the hunter"

Draco - means "dragon" - seen near North Star

Canis Major - southern sky - means "big dog"

Constellation Name	Also Named	Where to Look

Write Curve Forward Letters

Write the letters, joinings, and words.

n   n   n   n   n   n   n

Ne   Ni   Nu   No   Na   Ny

Newfoundland   Nice   Nome

Nigeria's flag is green and white.

m   m   m   m   m   m   m

Mi   Me   Mu   Mo   Ma   My

Missouri   Miami   Mexicali

Munich   Monaco   Manila

Better Letters

Pause and retrace after slant strokes. Write:

n not n   m not m

✓ Check your writing folder. Do you write these letters without loops?   Yes   No

Nigerian flag

Write the letters, joinings, and words.

H   H   H   H   H   H   H

He   Hi   Hu   Ho   Ha   Hy

Hebrides   Himalayas   Holland

K   K   K   K   K   K   K

Kl   Ki   Ku   Ka   Ko   Ky

Klondike   Kildare   Kansas

Katmandu is in the Himalayas.

DID YOU KNOW?

The Himalayas are in Asia.

Better Letters

Begin with a curve forward stroke. Write:

H not H   K not K

✔ Check your writing folder. Do you begin these
letters correctly?   Yes   No

Size

All uppercase letters are tall.
Circle your three best tall letters.

Write Curve Forward Letters

Write the letters, joinings, and words.

U

U   U   U   U   U   U   U   ✓

Uk   Up   Ug   Uc   Um   Uz   ✓

Ukraine   Uppsala   Utah

Y

Y   Y   Y   Y   Y   Y   Y   ✓

Yu   Ye   Yi   Yp   Ya   Yo   ✓

Yukon   Yangtze   Yosemite

Z

Z   Z   Z   Z   Z   Z   Z   ✓

Ze   Zu   Zi   Za   Zo   Zy   ✓

Zeeland   Zurich   Zambia

Better *Letters*

Pause after the undercurve in **U** and **Y**. Write:

U not U   Y not Y

✔ Check your writing folder. Do you write these letters correctly?   Yes   No

Size

Circle your three best uppercase letters that have a descender.

Write the letters and words.

$\mathcal{V}$ $\mathcal{V}$ $\mathcal{V}$ $\mathcal{V}$ $\mathcal{V}$ $\mathcal{V}$ $\mathcal{V}$ $\mathcal{V}$

Vietnam   *Vancouver*   *Virginia*

Vladivostok is a Russian port.

$\mathcal{W}$ $\mathcal{W}$ $\mathcal{W}$ $\mathcal{W}$ $\mathcal{W}$ $\mathcal{W}$ $\mathcal{W}$ $\mathcal{W}$

Waikiki   *Wyoming*   *Wuhsien*

Wales is in the United Kingdom.

$\mathcal{X}$ $\mathcal{X}$ $\mathcal{X}$ $\mathcal{X}$ $\mathcal{X}$ $\mathcal{X}$ $\mathcal{X}$

Xingu   *Xiamen*   *Xochimilco*

DID YOU KNOW?

Lake Xochimilco is in Mexico.

Better Letters

End **V** and **W** with an overcurve. Write:

$\mathcal{V}$ not $\mathcal{v}$ $\mathcal{W}$ not $\mathcal{w}$

✔ Check your writing folder. Do you end
these letters correctly?   Yes   No

A Welsh Cottage

Practice
Using Semicolons

This is a semicolon ;. You can sometimes make your writing easier to understand by using a semicolon to connect two sentences. Join each pair of sentences below into one sentence, using a semicolon. Here is an example.

New South Wales is a part of Australia. Its capital is Sydney.
New South Wales is a part of Australia; its capital is Sydney.

1. *The Waal River runs through Holland. It is used for shipping.*

2. *The Nile and the Mississippi are two rivers. The Nile is longer.*

3. *The Zambezi River is in Africa. It gave the country of Zambia its name.*

4. *The Thames Valley is in the United Kingdom. Tourists travel there.*

Writing Legibly

I. Study these tips for writing uppercase letters legibly. They will help you avoid common handwriting errors when you write.

✔ In cursive writing, use cursive uppercase letters. Write $\mathcal{W}$, not W .

✔ Make sure all uppercase letters are tall. Write $\mathcal{C}$, not $\smile$.

✔ Slant uppercase letters correctly. Write m, not $\mathcal{M}$.

✔ Leave space between uppercase letters that do not join and the letter that follows.
Write $October$, not $October$.

2. Look at this student's journal entry. Underline uppercase letters that need improvement.

Monday, October 9... How about that? Vic is my partner. Our project is on the Civil War. We'll get a good grade.

3. Rewrite the student's journal entry correctly, then write a journal entry of your own. Pay attention to the tips for legible writing.

Write Overcurve Letters

Write the letters, joinings, and words.

I   *I*   *I*   *I*   *I*   *I*   *I* ✓

Indus River   *Ireland*   *Izmir*

Israel is an ancient country.

J   *J*   *J*   *J*   *J*   *J*   *J* ✓

Je   *Ji*   *Ju*   *Ja*   *Jo* ✓

Jamaica   *Juneau*   *Jersey*

Q   *Q*   *Q*   *Q*   *Q*   *Q*   *Q* ✓

Quebec   *Quincy*   *Quad Cities*

Queensland is part of Australia.

Better Letters

Curve up and back for overcurve beginnings. Write:

I not *I*   *J* not *J*   *Q* not *Q*

✔ Check your writing folder. Do you begin these letters with a good overcurve?   Yes   No

38

Write Doublecurve Letters

Write the letters and words.

$\mathcal{T}$ $\mathcal{T}$ $\mathcal{T}$ $\mathcal{T}$ $\mathcal{T}$ $\mathcal{T}$ $\mathcal{T}$ $\mathcal{T}$

Texas   Thebes   Togo

Tipperary   The Tyne River

$\mathcal{F}$ $\mathcal{F}$ $\mathcal{F}$ $\mathcal{F}$ $\mathcal{F}$ $\mathcal{F}$ $\mathcal{F}$ $\mathcal{F}$

Finland   Mt. Fuji   Fairbanks

Florida   Frankfurt   Forth

DID YOU KNOW?

Togo is a country in Africa.

Mt. Fuji is located in Japan.

Better Letters

After lifting, begin the doublecurve directly on the preceding stroke. Write:

$\mathcal{T}$ not $\mathcal{T}$ $\mathcal{F}$ not $\mathcal{F}$

✔ Check your writing folder. Do you begin the doublecurve correctly?   Yes   No

Spacing

Circle your best spacing between letters that are not joined.

Practice
Places Around the World

A gazetteer gives information about places around the world. Here is part of a gazetteer.
Use the information to answer each question in your best cursive handwriting.

> *Florence:* Italian city, located on the Arno River
>
> *Iceland:* island republic, located between the Arctic and the Atlantic oceans
>
> *Illinois:* state in the midwestern United States
>
> *Java:* island, part of Indonesia
>
> *Quito:* capital of Ecuador, a country in South America
>
> *Taiwan:* island, part of China

Which island is part of Indonesia?

Which Italian city is located on the Arno River?

Which city is the capital of Ecuador?

Which island is located between two oceans?

Which U.S. state is in the Midwest?

Which island is part of China?

Which three places are islands?

Which two places are cities?

Which place is a state?

Keys to Legibility

My writing has good shape. ☐
My writing has good size. ☐
My writing has good spacing. ☐

Manuscript Maintenance

What Time Is It?

This is a time chart. It shows the time differences between ten different cities on one day.

Honolulu, Hawaii	Los Angeles, California	Phoenix, Arizona	Chicago, Illinois	New York, New York
A.M.	A.M.	A.M.	A.M.	P.M.
Caracas, Venezuela	Dublin, Ireland	Brussels, Belgium	Helsinki, Finland	Moscow, Russia
P.M.	P.M.	P.M.	P.M.	P.M.

Use the chart to answer each question. Write in manuscript.

It is 12:00 P.M. in New York.
What time is it in Chicago?

It is 5:00 P.M. in Dublin.
In which city is it 7:00 A.M.?

It is 8:00 P.M. in Moscow.
In which city is it 7:00 P.M.?

It is 11:00 A.M. in Chicago.
In which city is it 6:00 P.M.?

It is 9:00 A.M. in Los Angeles.
In which city is it 1:00 P.M.?

It is 7:00 A.M. in Honolulu.
What time is it in Phoenix?

Which city is two hours
ahead of Brussels?

Which city is two hours
behind Chicago?

Write Undercurve-Loop Letters

Write the letters and words.

G G G G G G G

Greenland   Guam   Germany

Gotha   Glasgow   Ghent

S S S S S S S

Spain   Sweden   Sydney

Sicily is an Italian island.

L L L L L L L L

Limerick   Laramie   London

DID YOU KNOW?

Limerick is an Irish port city.

Better Letters

Make the loop in **G** and **S** about one-half the letter height. Write:

G not L   S not S

✔ Check your writing folder. Do you write the loops correctly?   Yes   No

Slant

Circle three words you wrote that have good slant.

42

Write Undercurve-Slant Letters

Write the letters, joinings, and words.

P   P P P P P P P P ✓

Peoria   Peking   Paris

Patmos is a Greek island.

R   R R R R R R R ✓

Ri   Rh   Re   Ro   Ra   Ry ✓

Riviera   Rhine   Roanoke

B   B B B B B B B ✓

Belgrade   Bangladesh   Brisbane

Budapest   Great Britain

Better Letters

Retrace after the slant stroke to avoid loops. Write:

P not P   R not R   B not B

✔ Check your writing folder. Do you write these
letters correctly?   Yes   No

Practice
Facts About Space

Here are some facts about space. They are in scrambled sentences for you to unscramble. Be sure to begin your sentences with an uppercase letter. Here's a hint: you will use these uppercase letters: *G, S, L, P, R, B.*

1. *sunspots sun dark are on areas the.*

2. *light years space in distance measure.*

3. *planets the revolve around bodies celestial that sun are.*

4. *gravity Earth holds people on.*

5. *black holes light are without areas space in.*

6. *rays quickly space through travel.*

Keys to Legibility

My writing has good shape. ☐
My writing has good size. ☐
My writing has good spacing. ☐
My writing has good slant. ☐

Shape
Size
Spacing
Slant

Writing Legibly

I. Study these tips for writing uppercase letters legibly. They will help you avoid common handwriting errors when you write.

    ✔ In cursive writing, use cursive uppercase letters.

        Write *G*, not G.

        Write *R*, not R.

    ✔ Make sure all uppercase letters are tall.

        Write *The*, not *The*.

        Write *Sphinx*, not *Sphinx*.

2. Look at the beginning of this student's report. Underline letters that need improvement.

> *Giza*
>
> *Giza is a city on the Nile River, in Egypt. The Great Sphinx is there.*

3. Rewrite the student's work correctly, then write part of a paper of your own. Pay attention to the tips for legible writing.

Using Your Writing

Rewrite the message in your best cursive handwriting. It needs to be legible, so the penguins can be rescued.

In the following lessons, you will look closely at your handwriting. You will focus on shape, size, spacing, and slant to help you develop a legible personal style.

Personal Style

You and your classmates have learned to write Zaner-Bloser cursive letters. However, no one's handwriting is exactly like yours. As you practice writing, you develop a personal style that is yours alone.

Examine your personal style by writing these riddles and answers.

What goes up when the rain comes down? An umbrella!

_____

_____

_____

Why are fish considered to be so smart? They swim in schools!

_____

_____

_____

LEGIBLE LETTERS Personal differences are acceptable as long as your handwriting is legible.

Now look back at your writing. Check the items that describe your personal writing style.

☐ *I like to write small.*

☐ *I like to write big.*

☐ *I like to make fancy letters.*

Tell what else you notice about your personal style.

_____

_____

Ask a friend to read your writing and notice the shape of your letters.
Is the writing legible?   Yes   No

Write Numerals

Look at this list of the world's longest rivers.

River	Length in miles	Length in kilometers
1. Nile	4,145	6,673
2. Amazon	4,000	6,440
3. Mississippi-Missouri	3,740	6,021
4. Yangtze	3,720	5,989
5. Yenisei-Angara	3,650	5,877
6. Amur-Argun	3,590	5,780
7. Ob-Irtysh	3,360	5,410
8. Plata-Parana	3,030	4,878
9. Yellow	2,903	4,674
10. Congo	2,900	4,669

LEGIBLE LETTERS

Remember! Numerals are the same height as tall letters.

Use the list to answer these questions.

1. How many miles long is the Congo River?

It is

2. How many kilometers long is the Yellow River?

It is

3. Write the length in miles of the five longest rivers.

4. Write the length in kilometers of the five longest rivers.

On Your Own

Write the name of a river in your state. Then write your estimate of its length in miles.

Are your numerals the correct height?   Yes   No

4

Write an Editorial

An editorial is an article in a newspaper that tries to persuade readers about an important issue. The writer states his or her opinion directly and supports it with facts, details, and examples. Read this editorial. Look for the writer's opinion and the supporting facts.

      We must all work together to clean up Burnside River. First, we must stop throwing plastic bags and plastic can holders in the water. We must also stop tossing papers and garbage into the water. We should pick up trash and set out garbage cans, too. The city can post "No Littering" signs and charge fines for anyone caught littering. Adopt this slogan: Do your part to clean up Burnside River!

Write your own editorial about water pollution. Pay attention to the spacing between letters, words, and sentences.

_____

_____

_____

_____

_____

_____

_____

_____

_____

_____

Spacing

Is there space for ⃝ between letters?	Yes	No
Is there space for \ between words?	Yes	No
Is there space for ⃝ between sentences?	Yes	No

Write a List

You may have heard about the "Seven Wonders of the Ancient World." They are famous, but very few people can name them. They are:

1. The Pyramids of Giza, tombs for Egyptian kings (2600–2500 B.C.)
2. The Hanging Gardens of Babylon (605–562 B.C.)
3. The Temple of Artemis at Ephesus (550 B.C.)
4. The Statue of Zeus at Olympia (435 B.C.)
5. The Mausoleum at Halicarnassus (353 B.C.)
6. The Lighthouse of Alexandria (283–246 B.C.)
7. The Colossus of Rhodes, a bronze statue (200 B.C.)

Today, only the pyramids still stand.

List the Seven Wonders of the Ancient World. Use cursive writing.
Pay attention to the slant of your letters as you write. Draw a star next to the wonder people can still see today.

1.

2.

3.

4.

5.

6.

7.

Check your slant.

Draw lines through the slant strokes of the letters.

Your slant should look like *HHfoHH*. not *HfoHH*.

50

Edit Your Writing

Use these proofreading marks to edit your writing.

☰	Make a capital.	∧	Insert or add.
/	Use lowercase.	ℓ	Delete or take out.
⊙	Add a period.	¶	Indent for a new paragraph.

¶
reading
Long ago, people from many countries went to the library in Alexandria. They went there to study. Writing and ~~writing~~ had become very important. Some languages were very hard to read. egyptian hieroglyphics, mesopotamian cuneiform, and chinese characters were difficult. Greek writing used a simple Alphabet. Each symbol represented a sound. The Greek alphabet made it easy for people who spoke the language to read and write in Greek.

Write the paragraph, making the corrections shown by the proofreading marks.
Use your best cursive handwriting.

_____

_____

_____

_____

_____

_____

_____

_____

_____

_____

Shape
Size
Spacing
Slant

Ask a friend to proofread your writing.
Is the paragraph written correctly?   Yes   No
Is the paragraph legible?   Yes   No

Write in Other Languages

Here are names of foods in different languages.

English	French	Italian	Spanish	German
apple	pomme	mela	manzana	Apfel
beans	haricots	fagioli	frijoles	Bohnen
bread	pain	pane	pan	Brot
cheese	fromage	formaggio	queso	Käse
chicken	poulet	pollo	pollo	Huhn
eggs	oeufs	uova	huevos	Eier
milk	lait	latte	leche	Milch
pasta	pasta	pasta	pastas	Nudeln

1. Choose a language. Write three foods you might eat for breakfast.

_____

_____

2. Choose a language. Write three foods you might eat for lunch.

_____

_____

3. Choose a language. Write three foods you might eat for dinner.

_____

_____

4. Choose a language. Write three foods you might eat for a snack.

_____

On Your Own

Write the names of your three favorite foods.

_____

_____

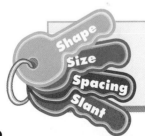

Is your writing legible?   Yes   No

The Writing Process: Writing a Travel Guide

A travel guide is written to tell people about a place to visit. A guide can be about a country, a city, or other special places. A travel guide may give the writer's opinion about the place. A guide gives facts about a place's most interesting sights.

Write a page to be included in a class travel guide. The guide will tell about interesting places to visit in your area.

Follow these steps for writing a travel guide.

I. Prewriting

First, you need to choose a place to write about. You might do this as a class, so that you all write about different places.

To plan your travel guide, write down the most important things a visitor needs to know about the place you have selected. Answer the questions below.

What is the name of the place?

_____

_____

Where is it located?

_____

_____

How can you travel there?

_____

_____

What sights can you see there?

_____

_____

What is your opinion of the place?

_____

_____

2. Drafting

Write your first draft.

COLLISION ALERT

Make sure your tall letters do not bump into the descenders above them.

_____

_____

_____

_____

_____

_____

_____

_____

_____

_____

_____

_____

_____

_____

_____

_____

Spacing			
Is there space for $\mathcal{O}$ between letters?		Yes	No
Is there space for \ between words?		Yes	No
Is there space for $\mathcal{O}$ between sentences?		Yes	No

3. Revising

Read your draft and mark any changes you want to make. You may want to ask a classmate to help you. Use editing marks as you revise your travel piece.

Use these proofreading marks to edit your writing.

☰	Make a capital.	∧	Insert or add.
/	Use lowercase.	ℰ	Delete or take out.
⊙	Add a period.	⁋	Indent for a new paragraph.

4. Editing

Check your travel guide page for errors in spelling, punctuation, capitalization, and handwriting. Use the questions below. You may want to ask a classmate to help you.

Did you provide all the basic information a visitor needs to know?	Yes	No
Did you add your own opinions?	Yes	No
Are all your tall letters the same size?	Yes	No
Are your small letters half the size of your tall letters?	Yes	No
Did you avoid collisions?	Yes	No
Is there good spacing between letters, words, and sentences?	Yes	No
Does your writing have uniform slant?	Yes	No
Is your writing legible?	Yes	No

5. Publishing

Publishing means using your best handwriting to prepare a neat, error-free copy of your writing that you can share with others. Here are some ideas for publishing your travel piece:

- With your classmates, staple all the travel pieces together to create a class travel guide. Pass the guide around so everyone can read it.

- Read your travel guide contribution aloud to a small group of classmates.

Manuscript Maintenance

Holidays Around the World

Read the passage about holidays in different countries.

There are interesting holidays all around the world. On March 3, Japan has a Doll Festival. Queen Isabella Day is held on April 22 in Spain. Oak Apple Day is held on May 29 in England. July 4 is Independence Day in the United States. In France, Bastille Day falls on July 14. The people of Nigeria celebrate Harvest Day on October 12.

Complete the chart below, using information from the passage. Write in manuscript.

Holiday	Country	Date

Posttest

On your paper, write the poem in your best cursive handwriting.

Metaphor

Morning is
a new sheet of paper
for you to write on.

Whatever you want to say,
all day,
until night
folds it up
and files it away.

The bright words and
the dark words
are gone
until dawn
and a new day
to write on.

Eve Merriam

Writing Quickly

Writing quickly is a skill that will help when you need to draft a story, write during a timed test, or take notes as your teacher talks. Writing that is done quickly should still be easy to read. With practice, you will learn how to make your writing speedy and legible.

Read the quotation below. It was first said by John F. Kennedy in 1961, in a speech he made when he became the 35ᵗʰ President of the United States. Write it quickly and legibly.

"And so, my fellow Americans, ask not what your country can do for you; ask what you can do for your country."

Write the quotation again. Try to write it faster, but make sure your writing is legible.

Write President Kennedy's statement two more times.
Try to write it even faster, but keep it easy to read.

Now read your writing. Circle Yes or No to respond to each statement. Then show your writing to someone, either a classmate or your teacher. Ask that person to circle Yes or No beside each statement.

	My Evaluation		My Classmate's or Teacher's Evaluation	
The writing is easy to read.	Yes	No	Yes	No
The writing has good Shape.	Yes	No	Yes	No
The writing has good Size.	Yes	No	Yes	No
The writing has good Spacing.	Yes	No	Yes	No
The writing has good Slant.	Yes	No	Yes	No

Writing Easily

As you write stories and essays for school papers and tests, it is important that your handwriting flows easily. When you automatically know how to write legibly, you don't have to worry about your handwriting. You are free to think about what you want your writing to say. With practice, you will learn how to make your writing easy, quick, and legible.

Read the writing prompt below. Respond to it by writing on the lines. Let your handwriting flow easily as you think and write.

Expository Writing

Think about two games you know very well.

Write a paragraph that compares and contrasts the two games. Include details and examples that explain how the games are alike and different.

Now read your writing. Circle Yes or No to respond to each statement. Then show your writing to someone, either a classmate or your teacher. Ask that person to circle Yes or No beside each statement.

	My Evaluation	My Classmate's or Teacher's Evaluation
The writing is easy to read.	Yes No	Yes No
The writing has good Shape.	Yes No	Yes No
The writing has good Size.	Yes No	Yes No
The writing has good Spacing.	Yes No	Yes No
The writing has good Slant.	Yes No	Yes No

Handwriting and the Writing Process
Write a Paragraph

A paragraph is a group of sentences about a main idea.
Write a paragraph about the American flag and what it means.

1. Prewriting

Prewriting means gathering ideas and planning before you write.
List your ideas on a piece of paper. Then plan your paragraph, telling the subject and in what order you will write your ideas.

2. Drafting

Drafting means putting your thoughts into written sentences for the first time. Use the ideas you listed in Prewriting to draft your paragraph. Write your first draft.

3. Revising

Revising means changing your writing to make it say exactly what you mean. Read your draft. Mark any changes you want to make.

Does your writing include all the information readers want to know?	Yes	No
Does your writing include descriptive details?	Yes	No

4. Editing

Editing means checking your revised writing for errors in spelling, punctuation, capitalization, and handwriting.

Are all words spelled correctly?	Yes	No
Have you used uppercase letters and punctuation correctly?	Yes	No
Do your letters have good shape and size?	Yes	No
Is there good spacing between letters, words, and sentences?	Yes	No
Does your writing have good uniform slant?	Yes	No
Is your writing easy to read?	Yes	No

5. Publishing

Publishing means using your best handwriting to make an error-free copy of your writing. Share your writing.

Record of Student's Handwriting Skills

Cursive

	Needs Improvement	Shows Mastery
Sits correctly	☐	☐
Holds pencil correctly	☐	☐
Positions paper correctly	☐	☐
Writes numerals **1-10**	☐	☐
Writes undercurve letters: **i, t, u, w**	☐	☐
Writes undercurve letters: **e, l, b, h, f**	☐	☐
Writes undercurve letters: **k, r, s, j, p**	☐	☐
Writes downcurve letters: **a, d, g, o, c, q**	☐	☐
Writes overcurve letters: **n, m, y, x, v, z**	☐	☐
Writes downcurve letters: **A, O, D, C, E**	☐	☐
Writes curve forward letters: **N, M, H, K**	☐	☐
Writes curve forward letters: **U, Y, Z, V, W, X**	☐	☐
Writes overcurve letters: **I, J, Q**	☐	☐
Writes doublecurve letters: **T, F**	☐	☐
Writes undercurve-loop letters: **G, S, L**	☐	☐
Writes undercurve-slant letters: **P, R, B**	☐	☐
Writes the undercurve to undercurve joining	☐	☐
Writes the undercurve to downcurve joining	☐	☐
Writes the undercurve to overcurve joining	☐	☐
Writes the overcurve to undercurve joining	☐	☐
Writes the overcurve to downcurve joining	☐	☐
Writes the overcurve to overcurve joining	☐	☐
Writes the checkstroke to undercurve joining	☐	☐
Writes the checkstroke to downcurve joining	☐	☐
Writes the checkstroke to overcurve joining	☐	☐
Writes with correct shape	☐	☐
Writes with correct size	☐	☐
Writes with correct spacing	☐	☐
Writes with uniform slant	☐	☐
Writes quickly	☐	☐
Writes with ease	☐	☐
Shows development in personal style	☐	☐
Regularly checks written work for legibility	☐	☐

Index